AN ALPHABET OF ANGELS

An Alphabet of

ANGELS

NANCY WILLARD

SCHOLASTIC INC.
New York Toronto London Auckland Sydney
Mexico City New Delhi Hong Kong

This book was originally published in hardcover by the Blue Sky Press in 1994.

ISBN 0-590-48481-8

12 11 10 9 8 7 6 5 4 3 2 1   0 1 2 3 4 5/0

Printed in the United States of America   08

First Scholastic paperback printing, November 2000

FOR JAMES AND JULIE

Every blade of grass has over it an angel saying, "Grow."

— THE TALMUD

The angel of alphabets opens the door.

Our A aim should be, I think, to make letters live.

The book angel whispers, "Go out and explore."

The angels of chimneys sing to the sweep.

The angel of dreaming flies in her sleep.

The angel of eggs repeats to the shell:
What's still as a secret and clear as a well?

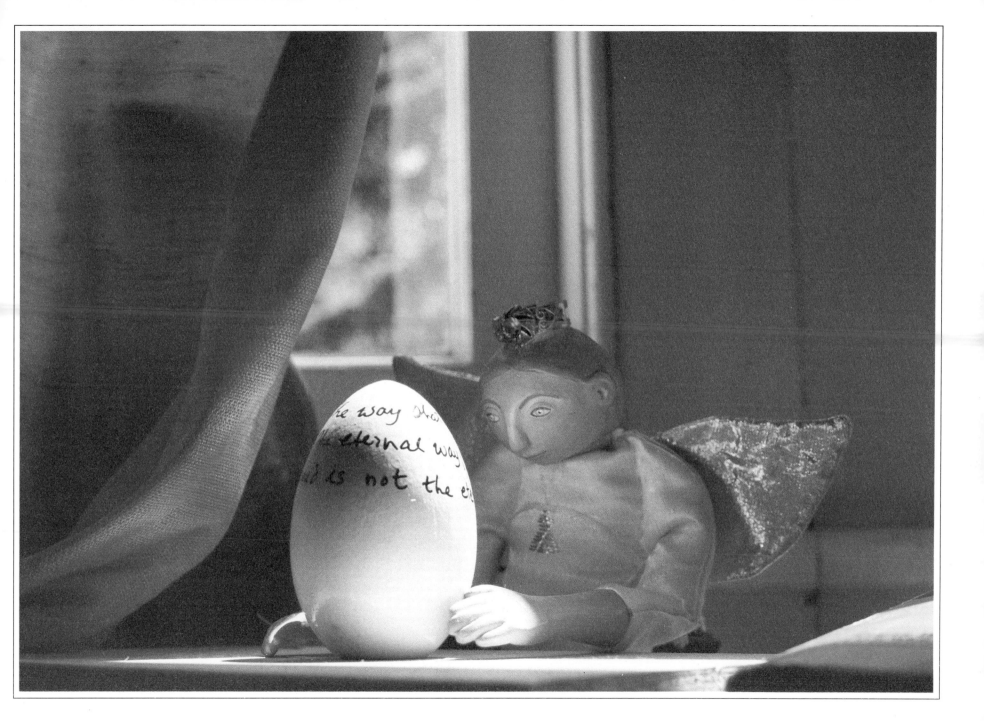

The angels of flowers have startled the grass.

The angel of games lets nobody pass.

The angel of halos gives up her gold bands.

I

The angel of ink is the servant of hands.

The angel of journeys is friend to the fish.

The angel of knapsacks delivers a wish

L

to the angel of letters, unfolding like lace

M

when the angel of morning wears dew on his face.

N

The angels of night
crow with delight.

The angel of oranges shakes them all free.

The angel of planets is small as a bee.

Q

The angel of quiet lets visitors go.

The angel of rooftops flies thrillingly low.

S

The angel of streetlights is polishing roads

T

for the angel of trumpets — their silence explodes.

The undersea angel leaves shelter behind.

The angel of vegetables ripens a rind.

The angel of windows opens them wide.

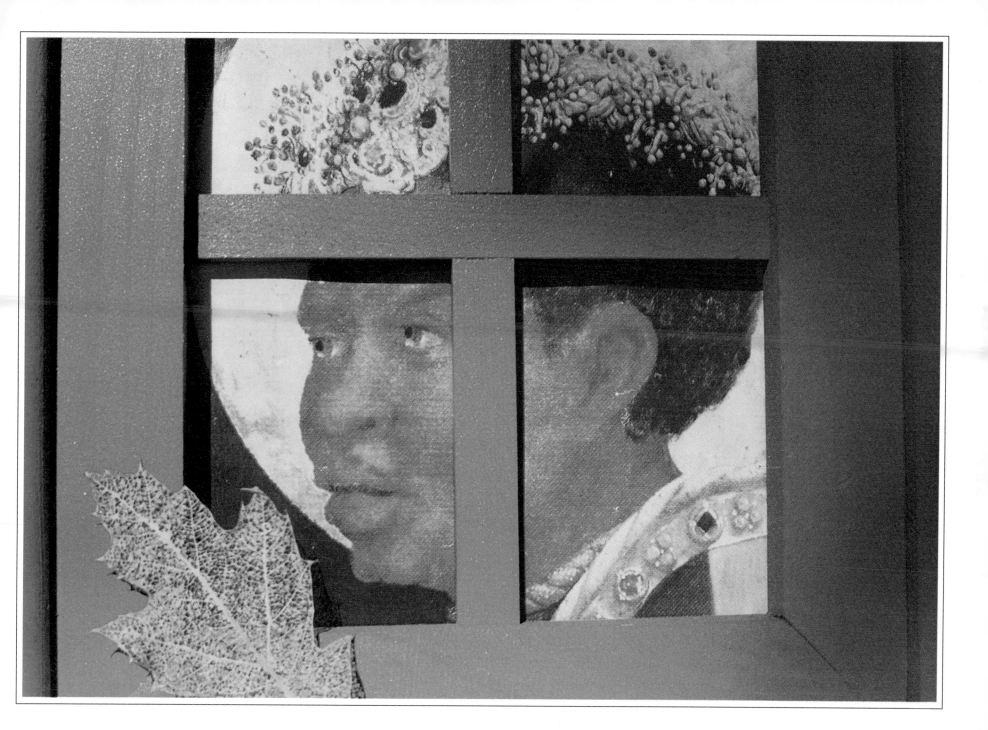

X

The angel of X rays takes us inside.

The angel of yonder looks after the light.

The zodiac angel sings us good night.

Four angels to my bed,
Gabriel stands at the head,
John and Peter at my feet,
All to watch me while I sleep.

— ANONYMOUS

THE END

ACKNOWLEDGMENTS

Doll, created by Tracy Gallup, was used as the angel of eggs.
Used by permission.

Dolls, created by Georgia Landau, were used as the angels of night.
Used by permission.

Original lithograph by Harold Altman was used as the background to the angel of quiet.
Used by permission.

Detail from "Empire of Lights," by René Magritte, was used as the background to the angel of streetlights.
Copyright © 1994 by C. Herscovici, Brussels/Artists Rights Society (ARS), New York.
Used by permission.

The background to the angel of yonder and the back jacket art of this book
is by Stephen Mackey, courtesy of Lip International, Manchester, England.
Used by permission.

•

The photographs in this book were taken by Nancy Willard.

The text type was set in Zapf Chancery Medium by WLCR New York, Inc.

Designed by Kathleen Westray